53

The new four rules of decimals

by K A Hesse

Longman

Contents

Check your four rules of number

Work across the page.

A	8 + 5 =	9 + 7 =	12 + 9 =	14 + 8 =	17 + 6 =
B	16 + 9 =	23 + 7 =	24 + 8 =	49 + 6 =	84 + 9 =
C	7 − 3 =	11 − 9 =	12 − 6 =	15 − 9 =	19 − 10 =
D	18 − 15 =	21 − 18 =	32 − 27 =	44 − 36 =	62 − 56 =
E	4 × 7 =	8 × 4 =	7 × 7 =	5 × 9 =	8 × 7 =
F	9 × 6 =	8 × 8 =	6 × 12 =	7 × 11 =	9 × 12 =
G	27 ÷ 9 =	42 ÷ 6 =	36 ÷ 7 =	40 ÷ 8 =	52 ÷ 6 =
H	54 ÷ 7 =	66 ÷ 9 =	105 ÷ 11 =	107 ÷ 12 =	118 ÷ 12 =

Add:

I			
	243	635	2475
	170	89	86
	306	40	709
	281	976	6790

Subtract:

634	706	8004
− 80	− 608	− 7096

Multiply:

J					
	407	687	985	374	275
	× 8	× 9	× 12	× 31	× 46

Divide:

K

6)150	9)3065	12)36110	23)484	31)6224

An introduction to decimals

Write down the value of the figure 6 in each of these numbers:

A	2,468	1,006	2,648
B	1,060	6,248	1,600

Write in figures:

C	forty	seventy-four
D	four hundred	forty-seven
E	four	four hundred and seven
F	four thousand	four thousand and seven

Any figure written down can have its value changed by placing zeros to the right of it, or by removing any figures to the right of it. We make 600 ten times bigger by placing a zero to the right of it (6,000), or ten times less by taking away a zero from the right of it (60).

Multiply each of these numbers by ten:

G	23	745	60	890	400	9

Divide each of these numbers by ten:

H	650	40	700	8090	35	100

The values of the figures in the number 5234 can be shown thus:

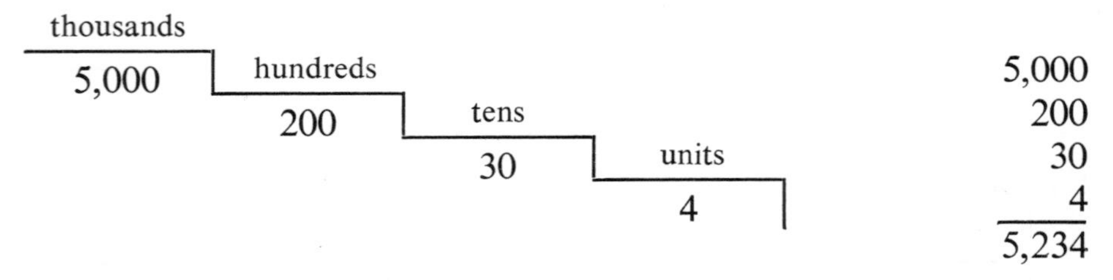

These are numbers used to tell of quantities greater than one, and we see that each place to the right is ten times less than the one before it. To show values less than one we can still move figures to the right and call them 'tenths', 'hundredths', 'thousandths', and so on. To show the figures have values less than one we place a dot or DECIMAL POINT after the units' figure and before the tenths', like this:

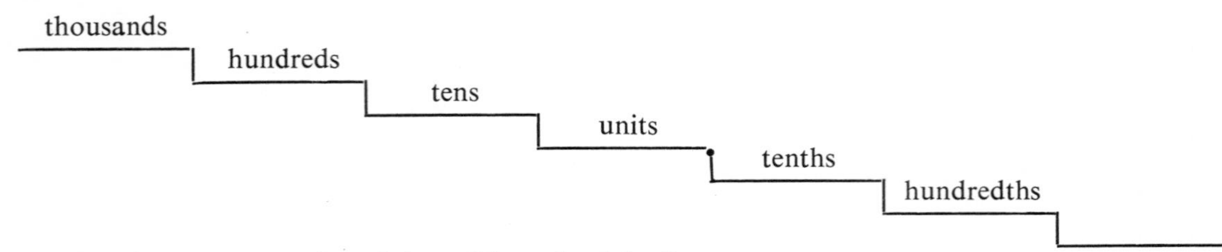

What value goes to the right of hundredths?

Look at the figures in these columns:

	thousands	hundreds	tens	units	.	tenths	hundredths
A			2	4	.	5	
B			2	4	.	6	7
C	1	5		3	.		
D			3		.	4	
E				5	.		6
F					.	8	9

In row A the number is written 24·5 (read: twenty-four point five)

and in row B 24·67 (read: twenty-four point six seven)

In row C there is not a figure in the tens' column so that we must put in a zero to keep the other figures to their correct place values, as

1503

We must do the same in rows D and E, so that we have

30·4
and 5·06

In row F we write 0·89 to make sure that it is not read as 89.

Make headings like these and put in these numbers with the figures in their correct places:

130 235·8 40·8 7·26 2·07 0·609 0·008

hundreds	tens	units	.	tenths	hundredths	thousandths
			.			
			.			
			.			
			.			
			.			
			.			
			.			

Read aloud these numbers and notice how we change the value as we move the figures one place to the right:

243 24·3 2·43 0·243 0·0243

Each time it makes a figure ten times less: the 40 or 4 tens becomes 4 or 4 units, the 3 units become 3 tenths, and in the last number the 4 is 4 thousandths and the 3 is 3 ten-thousandths.

In the same way, by moving the figures to the left, we make each figure worth ten times more at each move. Read aloud these numbers:

0·036 0·36 3·6 36·0 360·0 3,600·0

Complete these numbers:

A 2·25 = two whole ones, two tenths and hundreths.

B 4·7 = four whole ones and seven

C 3·06 = whole ones, tenths and hundredths.

D 0·089 = tenths, hundredths and nine

Write in decimal form:

E	6 tenths	7 hundredths	4 hundredths
F	3 tenths	8 thousandths	12 hundredths
G	23 hundredths	77 hundredths	6 thousandths
H	84 thousandths	15 thousandths	132 thousandths
I	17 tenths	409 thousandths	278 hundredths

J two and two tenths — three and three hundredths

K thirty and four tenths — ten and nine hundredths

By moving the figures, multiply each of these numbers by 10:

L	2·3	0·36	0·55	1·25	7·07	1·109
M	0·04	40	0·808	0·006	3	10·05

Divide each of these numbers by 10:

N	14·5	12·76	1·3	1·08	99	7·06
O	0·24	10·5	1·05	0·07	0·3	20·8

Multiply each of these numbers by 100:

P	1·32	5·4	10·89	0·7	0·006	1·05

Divide each of these numbers by 100:

Q	23·4	5·76	0·9	380	5·07	0·28

Multiply each of these numbers by 1000:

R	1·2437	5	5·078	0·62	0·081	1·029

Divide each of these numbers by 1000:

S	2,375	7,600	806	10·4	680	3

Some decimal units

Multiples			Whole unit	Sub-multiples		
1000	100	10	1	0·1	0·01	0·001
——	——	——	pound	——	new penny	——
kilometre	——	——	metre	——	centimetre	millimetre
kilogramme	——	——	gramme	——	——	milligramme
kilolitre	——	——	litre	——	——	millilitre

Complete:

A 1 centimetre (cm) = millimetres (mm) 1 metre (m) = centimetres

B 1 kilogramme (kg) = grammes (g) 1 gramme = kilogramme

C 1 litre (*l*) = kilolitre (k*l*) 1 kilolitre = *l*

D 1 pound (£) = new pence (p) 1 penny = pound

E 2 cm = mm 5 mm = cm 0·5 km = cm 12 mm = cm

F 0·2 k*l* = *l* 80 *l* = k*l* 35 cm = m 0·07 m = mm

G 1·6 cm = mm 0·03 kg = g 0·07 g = mg 82 mg = g

H 7,060 m = km 470 *l* = k*l* 30 mm = cm 300 *l* = k*l*

When we are writing pounds and new pence we have to remember that we use zeros differently from when writing metres, centimetres, etc.

30 cm = 0·3 m 30p = £0·30

Change to pence:

I £1·23 £0·47 £0·60 £0·07 £1·01

Change to pounds:

J 73p 130p 8p 40p 5p

Draw lines of the following lengths and against each line write its length in centimetres:

K 76 mm 106 mm 32 mm 0·014 m 0·009 m

Which is the greater number in each of these pairs?

L 0·54 and 0·504 0·2 and 0·04 0·6 and 0·30

M 7·1 and 5·06 3·78 and 3·709 2·8 and 2·75

The number half-way between 1 and 2 is 1·5. Write the nearest whole number to each of these numbers. If one is half-way take it to the next one up.

A	1·8	1·2	2·3	7·5	5·7	6·16
B	0·75	1·09	3·48	4·45	0·54	9·496

Write each of these amounts to the nearest penny:

C	7·3p	26·5p	30·8p	19·6p	20·4p	69·7p

In Decimal Currency, when writing amounts in pounds for ordinary occasions we use only two figures after the point and then the $\frac{1}{2}$p – as £0·23$\frac{1}{2}$. Only in offices are there likely to be more than two figures after the point.

1p = £0·01	and	1$\frac{1}{2}$p = £0·01$\frac{1}{2}$
1$\frac{1}{2}$p = 1·5p	so	1$\frac{1}{2}$p could be written as £0·015
	and	23$\frac{1}{2}$p could be written as £0·235

Look at these numbers:

0·111 0·112 0·113 0·114 0·115 0·116 0·117 0·118 0·119 0·12

D Which of them is half-way from 0·111 to 0·115?

E Which of them is half-way from 0·116 to 0·12?

To write a three-figure decimal part of a pound to the nearest halfpenny we write

a All amounts having the third figure less than 3 are brought down to the exact number of pennies, taking no notice of the third figure;

b all amounts that have the third figure between 3 to 7 inclusive are written as a $\frac{1}{2}$p, i.e. £0·574 becomes £0·57$\frac{1}{2}$ and £0·187 becomes £0·18$\frac{1}{2}$;

c all amounts with the third figure 8 or 9 are written to the next exact penny, i.e. £0·638 becomes £0·64 and £0·499 becomes £0·50.

Write each of these amounts to the nearest halfpenny:

F	£1·375	£0·231	£1·712	£2·664	£0·046
G	£0·808	£1·509	£1·065	£1·398	£0·707
H	£1·872	£1·048	£2·306	£2·299	£3·098

Check your addition

	Further practice
Set down in columns and add: **A** 8·7 + 5·2 + 5 **B** 3·7 + 2·06 + 6·1 **C** 5·07 + 0·9 + 3·4	*page 8 A–D*
D 3·8 + 7 + 2·5 **E** 2·52 + 0·81 + 3·73 **F** 0·24 + 2·07 + 0·09	*page 8 E–F*
G 3·64 + 0·78 + 6·65 **H** 0·86 + 9·5 + 0·07 **I** 4·57 + 10·8 + 0·09 + 2	*page 8 G–N*
J 4·38 + 0·9 + 0·076 + 0·65 **K** 0·0806 + 0·7 + 0·917 + 0·303 **L** 0·875 + 6·3 + 0·008 + 0·82	*page 9 A–D*
M 0·416 + 2·07 + 0·8005 + 1·6639 **N** 10·75 + 0·8936 + 4·077 + 14·3 **O** 11·07 + 10·87 + 0·9 + 20·96	*page 9 E–J*
P £3·70 + £0·08 + £2·90 + £0·82 **Q** 0·63 cm + 1·04 cm + 3·85 cm + 10·5 cm **R** 10·2 kg + 0·75 kg + 3·065 kg + 0·99 kg	*page 10 A–H*
Give your answers in millimetres, pounds or grammes. **S** 20·8 mm + 3 mm + 0·65 cm + 1·075 cm **T** £3 + $8\frac{1}{2}$p + 70p + $16\frac{1}{2}$p + £0·09$\frac{1}{2}$ **U** 30 g + 2·04 kg + 507·5 g + 80 g + 0·03 kg	*page 10 I–T*

Addition

Add:

A	1·2	4·1	3·5	4·15	5·6	4·08
	2·3	3·6	7	2·3	7	0·6
	1·1	5	2·2	3·04	2·08	6·2

Set down in columns and add:

B 2·3 + 1·2 + 3·4   4 + 5·3 + 4·5

C 1·13 + 1·14 + 2·12   3·7 + 2·06 + 5·1

D 2·24 + 3·3 + 6·05   2·06 + 0·8 + 8·13

E	0·3	0·3	0·8	1·4	3·6	0·7
	0·1	0·6	0·7	3·5	0·8	6·4
	0·5	0·4	0·6	2·6	5·4	0·9

F	0·13	0·17	0·04	2·5	1·63	0·41
	0·27	0·04	0·33	1·34	3·4	0·72
	0·42	0·15	0·5	2·41	0·52	0·64

G	0·57	0·87	4·58	0·8	0·64	6·84
	0·49	0·06	0·09	6·07	7	7·6
	0·68	0·55	5·8	0·9	3·08	0·08

Set down in columns and add:

H 0·16, 0·35 and 0·24   0·06, 0·73 and 2·15

I 2·35, 2·5 and 1·36   2·43, 0·72 and 0·06

J 4·5, 0·67 and 3·06   0·7, 3·58 and 6·6

K 0·09, 5·8 and 6·7   5, 4·07 and 0·8

L 3·67, 4 and 0·09   3·68, 0·79 and 8·5

M 2·3, 0·08 and 6·75   0·48, 6·9 and 0·07

N 0·86, 9·5 and 0·07   4·58, 0·09 and 5·8

Add:

A	2·1	3·6	0·45	0·34	0·53	2·03
	3·5	4	0·02	0·5	0·07	0·8
	1·4	2·4	0·33	0·16	0·4	5·17

B	5·24	6·3	3·06	5·86	4·75	8·79
	3·07	0·08	0·79	8·98	0·02	3·86
	0·69	3·62	6·18	5·17	5·23	7·35

C	1·162	2·312	3·415	2·354	1·02
	4·312	0·041	1·006	0·75	20·3
	5·213	1·206	2·532	3·467	2·86

D	0·285	0·5	0·34	5·48	0·8
	2·53	0·06	6·7	0·875	6·75
	1·723	3·7	0·008	2·6	12·8
	3·078	2·835	0·953	0·065	0·09

E	7·875	0·96	7·15	0·037	11·3
	0·68	8·5	0·8	0·6005	0·87
	0·909	0·064	0·086	0·8	0·9
	4·08	0·97	0·965	0·563	27·96

Set down these examples in columns and add:

F 5·3, 0·076 and 0·8   2·06, 3·5 and 4·44

G 0·736, 0·8 and 6·47   12·75, 0·9 and 8·67

H 0·6007, 0·089 and 2·5   7·3, 0·06, 0·8 and 0·75

I 0·6905, 3·078, 2·8275 and 0·095

J 2·376, 0·0075, 12·75 and 0·875

Write in columns and add:

A $7{\cdot}63\text{ km} + 0{\cdot}89\text{ km} + 11{\cdot}766\text{ km} + 3{\cdot}6\text{ km}$

B £23·84 + £7·06 + £80 + £5·37

C £4·08 + £0·29½ + £1·06½ + £10·40

D $32\ l + 2{\cdot}56\ l + 0{\cdot}78\ l + 8{\cdot}3\ l$

E $2{\cdot}7\text{ m} + 18\text{ m} + 3{\cdot}1\text{ m} + 0{\cdot}985\text{ m} + 1{\cdot}076\text{ m}$

F $43\text{ mm} + 7{\cdot}6\text{ mm} + 0{\cdot}58\text{ mm} + 2{\cdot}35\text{ mm} + 20\text{ mm}$

G £0·86½ + £1·70 + £4 + £1·08½

H $0{\cdot}73\text{ kg} + 1{\cdot}275\text{ kg} + 3{\cdot}9\text{ kg} + 2{\cdot}076\text{ kg}$

When writing into columns express all items in the same unit value as that of the first item. The diagram on page 5 will help you.

I £1·72 + 46p + 83p + £1·08

J 23p + 7p + £0·06 + £0·45

K $0{\cdot}25\text{ g} + 1{\cdot}075\text{ g} + 30\text{ mg} + 306\text{ mg}$

L $1{\cdot}125\text{ m} + 103\text{ cm} + 9{\cdot}6\text{ cm} + 0{\cdot}75\text{ m}$

M $10{\cdot}65\text{ cm} + 0{\cdot}875\text{ cm} + 3\text{ mm} + 18{\cdot}5\text{ mm}$

N $115{\cdot}3\ l + 10{\cdot}5\ l + 1{\cdot}375\text{ k}l + 0{\cdot}186\text{ k}l + 15\ l$

O $1{\cdot}506\text{ k}l + 23{\cdot}6\ l + 207{\cdot}5\ l + 34{\cdot}7\ l + 9\ l$

P £2 + 8½p + 72½p + 93p + £0·10½

Q $1{\cdot}5\text{ kg} + 20\text{ g} + 108\text{ g} + 0{\cdot}125\text{ kg} + 70\text{ g}$

R $30\text{ m} + 109\text{ m} + 0{\cdot}25\text{ km} + 300\text{ m} + 1{\cdot}075\text{ km}$

S $17\text{ mm} + 8{\cdot}5\text{ mm} + 1{\cdot}6\text{ cm} + 0{\cdot}21\text{ cm} + 1{\cdot}08\text{ cm}$

T $1{\cdot}085\text{ km} + 2\text{ km} + 207\text{ m} + 670{\cdot}5\text{ m}$

U $2{\cdot}6\ l + 0{\cdot}098\ l + 308\text{ m}l + 965\text{ m}l$

V $70\ l + 0{\cdot}125\text{ k}l + 705\text{ m}l + 875\text{ m}l + 0{\cdot}75\ l$

	Further practice
Work across the page. Put the numbers in each group in order of size – smallest first: **A** 1·3, 3·1, 0·31 2·0, 0·02, 1·20, 1·002	*page 12 A–D*
B 4·3 − 2·7 1·4 − 0·8 6·23 − 5·19 3·55 − 0·48	*page 12 E–G*
In these pairs subtract the smaller from the larger: **C** 3·24 and 5·04 8·04 and 6·75 4·06 and 3·98 5·03 and 4·97	*page 12 H–M*
D 4 − 2·37 3·5 − 1·42 6·6 − 5·54 8·5 − 7·96	*page 13 A–F*
In these pairs subtract the smaller from the larger: **E** 0·206 and 0·35 4 and 3·92 **F** 0·437 and 0·56 0·096 and 0·401	*page 13 G–M*
In these pairs subtract the smaller from the larger: **G** £2·18 and £2·07½ 5·4 km and 5·291 km **H** 0·58 *l* and 0·409 *l* 27·2 kg and 26·923 kg	*page 14 A–I*
In these pairs change the amount at the higher unit value into that of the lower unit value and subtract: **I** 0·47 km and 506 m £0·09½ and 12p **J** 203 *l* and 1·05 k*l* 1·3 m and 9·8 cm	*page 14 J–Q*

Subtraction

Write each of these groups in order of size – smallest first:

A 1·2, 0·12, 2·1, 0·21 — 0·22, 2·2, 0·02, 0·2

B 0·8, 0·080, 0·008, 8·0 — 3·0, 0·03, 0·75, 5·7

C 10·8, 1·08, 9·08, 9·80 — 1·25, 0·525, 0·55, 0·125

D 1·10, 11·1, 1·12, 11·3 — 0·110, 1·0, 1·01, 0·011

Take away:

E $6·8 - 2·5$ | $3·7 - 2·7$ | $6·1 - 2·9$ | $8·4 - 5·8$ | $6·3 - 5·3$ | $6·6 - 5·7$

F $7·1 - 6·4$ | $4·1 - 0·6$ | $1·2 - 0·5$ | $1·5 - 0·9$ | $1·6 - 0·8$ | $1·7 - 0·9$

G $4·35 - 2·35$ | $6·57 - 2·48$ | $5·45 - 5·38$ | $7·73 - 6·76$ | $4·64 - 3·68$ | $5·77 - 0·69$

H $3·62 - 0·54$ | $6·27 - 0·28$ | $4·53 - 0·49$ | $5·04 - 2·94$ | $3·03 - 2·85$ | $6·04 - 4·87$

I $5·04 - 4·96$ | $6·07 - 3·99$ | $8·05 - 7·98$ | $5·14 - 4·07$ | $8·55 - 7·08$ | $4·32 - 3·38$

J $4·06 - 1·26$ | $6·07 - 5·18$ | $5·06 - 4·07$ | $6·07 - 5·09$ | $7·03 - 4·95$ | $9·08 - 8·99$

In these pairs subtract the smaller number from the larger:

K 7·5 and 3·7 | 4·5 and 0·7 | 0·4 and 0·6

L 0·7 and 2·1 | 6·04 and 4·86 | 5·93 and 7·01

M 5·09 and 6·08 | 0·78 and 1·02 | 2·02 and 1·98

Take away:

A	5·06 − 3·5	7·27 − 4·2	5·05 − 4·4	6·0 − 1·8	5 − 1·4	6 − 4·3
B	7·03 − 6·7	6 − 0·5	5 − 0·7	4 − 0·8	6·5 − 3·47	8·2 − 5·06
C	3·3 − 1·07	6·6 − 5·54	7·2 − 6·26	4 − 0·38	5·4 − 0·92	7·3 − 6·91

D	0·526 − 0·324	0·603 − 0·453	0·703 − 0·65	0·606 − 0·57	0·072 − 0·055
E	0·024 − 0·016	0·13 − 0·012	0·28 − 0·028	0·05 − 0·037	0·44 − 0·044
F	0·29 − 0·029	0·93 − 0·093	0·6 − 0·066	6·5 − 2·008	4·03 − 3·092

In these pairs subtract the smaller number from the larger:

G	0·501 and 0·46	7 and 4·6	0·75 and 0·9
H	3 and 0·83	0·6 and 0·37	0·306 and 0·52
I	1·2 and 1·089	2·01 and 0·837	0·06 and 0·047
J	0·8 and 0·703	0·093 and 0·41	3·02 and 0·801
K	0·505 and 0·75	0·54 and 0·202	1·03 and 0·993
L	2·7 and 1·902	1·002 and 1·1	4·4 and 0·396
M	6 and 0·991	0·16 and 0·089	2·7 and 2·097

Take away:

A

£2·76$\frac{1}{2}$	£4·35	£3·08	£1·03$\frac{1}{2}$	£5·20	£4·05
− 1·56$\frac{1}{2}$	− 1·32$\frac{1}{2}$	− 0·72$\frac{1}{2}$	− 0·67	− 2·18$\frac{1}{2}$	− 3·66$\frac{1}{2}$

In these pairs subtract the smaller amount from the larger:

B £3·61 and £2·69 — £2·18$\frac{1}{2}$ and £2·52$\frac{1}{2}$

C 6·05 m and 6·12 m — 0·75 *l* and 0·594 *l*

D 23·1 km and 23·087 km — 0·8 g and 0·604 g

E 4·15 k*l* and 4·136 k*l* — 1·1 cm and 1·091 cm

F £1·30 and £1·09$\frac{1}{2}$ — 5·3 kg and 5·198 kg

G 0·6 km and 0·0698 km — 0·67 *l* and 0·703 *l*

H 1·03 k*l* and 1·0193 k*l* — £1·06$\frac{1}{2}$ and £1·60

I 18·03 m and 18·029 m — 5·12 kg and 5·099 kg

Write which is the lower unit value in each of these pairs:

J m and cm — m and km — mm and cm

K k*l* and *l* — g and mg — g and kg

In these pairs change the higher unit to that of the lower and subtract:

L 0·146 cm and 10·7 mm — 23 mg and 0·168 g

M £0·37$\frac{1}{2}$ and 40$\frac{1}{2}$p — 437 *l* and 0·3748 k*l*

N 15 g and 0·207 kg — 0·32 km and 209 m

O 0·6 cm and 4·85 mm — £0·08$\frac{1}{2}$ and 11p

P £1·06 and 0·19$\frac{1}{2}$p — 0·81 m and 78·6 cm

Q 0·8 kg and 85·7 g — 110·5 *l* and 0·1015 k*l*

R 307 m*l* and 2·01 *l* — £0·68$\frac{1}{2}$ and 85p

S 1·7 g and 1,809 mg — 1,045 m*l* and 0·75 *l*

Work across the page.

		Further practice
A	Write answers only: $3 \times 0{\cdot}6 =$ $0{\cdot}4 \times 7 =$ $8 \times 0{\cdot}5 =$ $0{\cdot}9 \times 12 =$	*page 16 A–F*
B	$2{\cdot}4 \times 2$ $5{\cdot}8 \times 7$ $3{\cdot}05 \times 6$ $2{\cdot}125 \times 12$	*page 16 G–I*
C	$176 \times 0{\cdot}8$ $8{\cdot}4 \times 0{\cdot}6$ $0{\cdot}65 \times 0{\cdot}8$ $0{\cdot}85 \times 0{\cdot}9$	*page 16 J–N*
D	$30{\cdot}7 \times 0{\cdot}06$ $1{\cdot}18 \times 0{\cdot}07$ $2{\cdot}94 \times 0{\cdot}11$ $0{\cdot}056 \times 0{\cdot}12$	*page 17 A–F*
E	Find the product of: 1·1 and 0·276 0·09 and 0·79 0·12 and 3·09	*page 17 G–N*
F	State your answers in metres, litres or grammes: 0·86 km × 0·7 0·607 k*l* × 1·1 90·5 mg × 1·2	*page 18 A–I*
G	£0·20½ × 8 £1·07½ × 11 £1·65 × 12	*page 18 J–N*
H	Find the square of: 0·5 0·7 1·1	*page 18 O–P*
I	$3{\cdot}24 \times 1{\cdot}7$ $0{\cdot}206 \times 50$ $0{\cdot}628 \times 0{\cdot}35$	*page 19 A–F*

See page iv for suggestions on how best to use this page.

Multiplication

Write answers only:

A	$1 \times 1 =$	$0{\cdot}1 \times 1 =$	$0{\cdot}2 \times 3 =$	$0{\cdot}4 \times 3 =$	$0{\cdot}3 \times 6 =$
B	$2 \times 0{\cdot}4 =$	$3 \times 0{\cdot}4 =$	$5 \times 0{\cdot}3 =$	$0{\cdot}7 \times 3 =$	$5 \times 0{\cdot}5 =$
C	$2 \times 5 =$	$0{\cdot}2 \times 5 =$	$5 \times 0{\cdot}2 =$	$0{\cdot}5 \times 2 =$	$0{\cdot}4 \times 5 =$
D	$5 \times 6 =$	$0{\cdot}8 \times 5 =$	$5 \times 0{\cdot}8 =$	$0{\cdot}5 \times 12 =$	$6 \times 0{\cdot}5 =$
E	$2 \times 10 =$	$0{\cdot}2 \times 10 =$	$0{\cdot}4 \times 10 =$	$0{\cdot}7 \times 10 =$	$0{\cdot}8 \times 11 =$
F	$0{\cdot}5 \times 8 =$	$0{\cdot}6 \times 10 =$	$1{\cdot}2 \times 10 =$	$4{\cdot}3 \times 10 =$	$0{\cdot}9 \times 12 =$

Multiply:

G	$6{\cdot}4 \times 7$	$7{\cdot}8 \times 9$	$2{\cdot}13 \times 8$	$6{\cdot}45 \times 9$	$7{\cdot}06 \times 8$	$8{\cdot}84 \times 12$
H	$4{\cdot}5 \times 4$	$5{\cdot}5 \times 6$	$7{\cdot}5 \times 8$	$7{\cdot}5 \times 12$	$5{\cdot}05 \times 6$	$4{\cdot}06 \times 5$
I	$7{\cdot}75 \times 8$	$9{\cdot}25 \times 12$	$3{\cdot}026 \times 5$	$4{\cdot}009 \times 7$	$6{\cdot}125 \times 8$	$7{\cdot}085 \times 12$
J	$146 \times 0{\cdot}7$	$145 \times 0{\cdot}6$	$175 \times 0{\cdot}8$	$158 \times 0{\cdot}9$	$265 \times 0{\cdot}8$	$289 \times 0{\cdot}9$
K	$4{\cdot}6 \times 0{\cdot}7$	$3{\cdot}7 \times 0{\cdot}9$	$5{\cdot}6 \times 0{\cdot}8$	$3{\cdot}6 \times 0{\cdot}5$	$3{\cdot}4 \times 0{\cdot}6$	$7{\cdot}5 \times 0{\cdot}8$
L	$1{\cdot}4 \times 0{\cdot}3$	$1{\cdot}6 \times 0{\cdot}6$	$1{\cdot}2 \times 0{\cdot}8$	$0{\cdot}67 \times 0{\cdot}9$	$0{\cdot}96 \times 0{\cdot}5$	$0{\cdot}95 \times 0{\cdot}8$

Find the product of:

M	3·05 and 5	158 and 0·9	138 and 0·5	4·5 and 0·6
N	7·25 and 0·8	0·89 and 0·7	0·75 and 0·8	0·79 and 0·9

Multiply:

A

0·35	0·23	0·16	0·25	0·13	0·12
× 0·6	× 0·4	× 0·6	× 1·2	× 0·7	× 0·8

Write answers only:

B 0·6 × 7 = 0·07 × 0·6 = 0·08 × 0·5 = 0·09 × 0·7 =

C 0·05 × 0·8 = 0·09 × 0·8 = 0·07 × 0·9 = 0·08 × 0·9 =

Multiply:

D

2·06	1·05	4·05	32·9	21·8
× 0·4	× 0·6	× 0·8	× 0·07	× 0·09

E

3·24	2·18	3·94	1·05	3·75
× 0·06	× 0·05	× 0·11	× 0·06	× 0·12

F

0·213	0·312	0·706	4·69	0·036
× 4	× 0·9	× 0·8	× 0·11	× 0·12

Find the product of:

G 0·036 and 0·7 1·2 and 0·136 0·5 and 0·476

H 0·765 and 0·8 0·476 and 0·6 0·8 and 0·068

I 0·9 and 0·06 0·0958 and 0·7 0·9 and 0·0687

J 0·087 and 0·12 0·11 and 0·308 0·098 and 0·12

K 0·508 and 0·04 0·307 and 0·06 0·08 and 0·308

L 0·12 and 0·805 2·36 and 0·08 4·08 and 0·05

M 7·08 and 0·07 0·09 and 0·69 0·12 and 3·05

N 0·11 and 0·95 2·08 and 0·12 1·095 and 0·11

Multiply:

A £1·32 × 5 0·43 kg × 0·7 6·35 cm × 8

B 1·08 km × 9 £3·06 × 8 2·08 k*l* × 0·11

C 0·705 m × 1·2 23·78 cm × 10 £20·70 × 12

D £10·80 × 11 0·725 k*l* × 12 2·075 kg × 1·1

Multiply and state your answer in metres:

E 3·8 cm × 10 40·5 cm × 8 30·5 mm × 12

F 2·37 km × 0·4 1·48 km × 0·7 0·85 km × 0·8

Multiply and state your answers in grammes:

G 0·328 kg × 7 37·8 mg × 10 1·67 kg × 0·8

H 30·5 mg × 12 1·375 g × 0·9 506·8 mg × 12

Multiply and state your answers in litres:

I 1·085 *l* × 0·8 0·706 k*l* × 0·7 0·096 k*l* × 1·1

Multiply:

J $\frac{1}{2}$p × 3 $\frac{1}{2}$p × 5 $\frac{1}{2}$p × 8 $\frac{1}{2}$p × 10 $\frac{1}{2}$p × 9

K 1$\frac{1}{2}$p × 5 1$\frac{1}{2}$p × 6 1$\frac{1}{2}$p × 9 2$\frac{1}{2}$p × 12 6$\frac{1}{2}$p × 11

L £0·03$\frac{1}{2}$ × 7 £0·02$\frac{1}{2}$ × 6 £0·07$\frac{1}{2}$ × 8 £0·02$\frac{1}{2}$ × 10

M £0·05$\frac{1}{2}$ × 11 £0·08$\frac{1}{2}$ × 9 £0·06$\frac{1}{2}$ × 11 £0·09$\frac{1}{2}$ × 10

N £1·07$\frac{1}{2}$ × 9 £2·10$\frac{1}{2}$ × 10 £1·17$\frac{1}{2}$ × 12 £0·30$\frac{1}{2}$ × 10

Find the area of each rectangle as shown by the sketches:

O

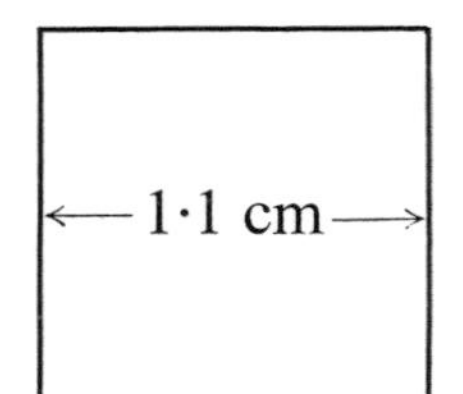

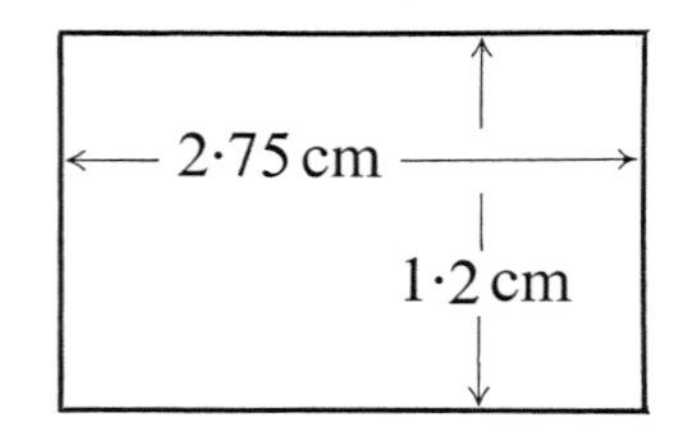

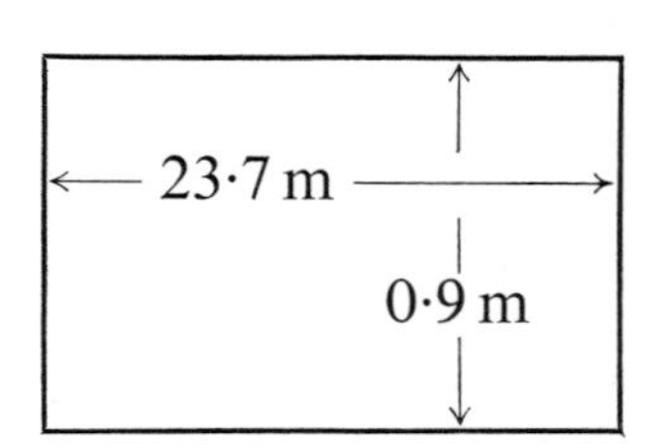

Find the square of:

P 0·6 0·8 0·09 1·2 0·1 0·7

Long multiplication

Multiply:

A	324 × 2·1	24·3 × 16	3·14 × 31	30·8 × 2·6
B	0·353 × 18	2·63 × 1·6	7·06 × 3·4	4·27 × 0·26
C	3·67 × 0·18	4·25 × 0·26	0·353 × 1·8	0·547 × 3·2
D	31·2 × 20	41·3 × 30	3·06 × 20	0·205 × 20
E	5·05 × 2·6	3·06 × 2·5	5·16 × 0·25	1·068 × 3·5
F	0·174 × 2·3	0·528 × 0·36	0·637 × 0·26	8·01 × 0·025

Check your division

	Further practice
Work across the page. **A** $4\overline{)5{\cdot}6}$ $7\overline{)23{\cdot}8}$ $9\overline{)3{\cdot}06}$ $8\overline{)0{\cdot}0368}$	*page 21*
Take answers to the second SIGNIFICANT figure: **B** $5\overline{)20{\cdot}1}$ $7\overline{)0{\cdot}601}$ $9\overline{)0{\cdot}703}$ $12\overline{)1{\cdot}09}$	*page 22*
Express each answer to the nearest centimetre: **C** 57·6 cm ÷ 9 0·04 km ÷ 8 1·13 m ÷ 12 Express each answer to the nearest litre: **D** 0·771 k*l* ÷ 6 11·92 *l* ÷ 8 10·806 k*l* ÷ 12	*page 23 A–I*
Express each answer to the nearest halfpenny: **E** £1·05 ÷ 6 £1·68 ÷ 9 £2·38 ÷ 12	*page 23 J–R*
Take answers to the fourth decimal place: **F** $6\overline{)0{\cdot}92}$ $7\overline{)5{\cdot}8\dot{5}}$ $11\overline{)12{\cdot}\dot{8}\dot{3}}$ $12\overline{)0{\cdot}9\dot{1}\dot{8}}$	*page 24*
Write answers in rows **G** to **I** correct to the third decimal place: **G** $8\overline{)0{\cdot}82}$ $6\overline{)2{\cdot}344}$ $11\overline{)6{\cdot}597}$ $12\overline{)12{\cdot}237}$	*page 25*
H $0{\cdot}7\overline{)30{\cdot}1}$ $1{\cdot}1\overline{)0{\cdot}631}$ $0{\cdot}9\overline{)6{\cdot}\dot{6}}$ $1{\cdot}2\overline{)70}$	*page 26*
I $0{\cdot}23\overline{)0{\cdot}805}$ $2{\cdot}7\overline{)8{\cdot}168}$ $0{\cdot}53\overline{)3{\cdot}718}$	*page 27*

Division

Work across the page.

Write answers only:

A	$8 \div 4 =$	$0{\cdot}8 \div 4 =$	$0{\cdot}6 \div 3 =$	$0{\cdot}9 \div 3 =$
B	$12 \div 2 =$	$1{\cdot}2 \div 2 =$	$1{\cdot}2 \div 4 =$	$1{\cdot}2 \div 6 =$
C	$1{\cdot}5 \div 3 =$	$1{\cdot}5 \div 5 =$	$2{\cdot}4 \div 6 =$	$2{\cdot}8 \div 7 =$
D	$1{\cdot}6 \div 4 =$	$3{\cdot}6 \div 4 =$	$3{\cdot}6 \div 9 =$	$0{\cdot}36 \div 9 =$
E	$32 \div 8 =$	$3{\cdot}2 \div 8 =$	$0{\cdot}32 \div 8 =$	$0{\cdot}32 \div 4 =$
F	$3{\cdot}5 \div 7 =$	$0{\cdot}35 \div 7 =$	$0{\cdot}35 \div 5 =$	$0{\cdot}54 \div 9 =$
G	$0{\cdot}54 \div 6 =$	$0{\cdot}48 \div 8 =$	$0{\cdot}63 \div 7 =$	$0{\cdot}81 \div 9 =$

Divide:

H	$2\overline{)2{\cdot}6}$	$3\overline{)6{\cdot}3}$	$4\overline{)4{\cdot}8}$	$5\overline{)6{\cdot}5}$	$6\overline{)8{\cdot}4}$
I	$7\overline{)9{\cdot}8}$	$6\overline{)9{\cdot}6}$	$4\overline{)13{\cdot}6}$	$6\overline{)31{\cdot}8}$	$8\overline{)27{\cdot}2}$
J	$9\overline{)40{\cdot}5}$	$3\overline{)12{\cdot}6}$	$3\overline{)1{\cdot}26}$	$7\overline{)2{\cdot}24}$	$9\overline{)3{\cdot}87}$
K	$4\overline{)0{\cdot}48}$	$6\overline{)0{\cdot}84}$	$6\overline{)0{\cdot}804}$	$8\overline{)0{\cdot}864}$	$7\overline{)0{\cdot}903}$
L	$3\overline{)0{\cdot}126}$	$5\overline{)0{\cdot}205}$	$6\overline{)0{\cdot}306}$	$7\overline{)0{\cdot}406}$	$9\overline{)0{\cdot}603}$
M	$4\overline{)0{\cdot}216}$	$6\overline{)0{\cdot}444}$	$8\overline{)0{\cdot}096}$	$9\overline{)0{\cdot}072}$	$7\overline{)0{\cdot}504}$

Divide:

A	2)6·3	4)0·86	6)0·9	8)0·884	6)1·83
B	5)2·51	7)0·644	8)0·124	12)0·294	9)9·036
C	4)6·1	4)0·103	6)0·237	8)7·63	4)3·7
D	6)0·099	8)8·362	12)3·99	8)0·778	12)10·05

Take answers to the third decimal place, i.e. show the third digit after the decimal point, including zeros:

E	3)0·342	6)0·85	7)2·19	9)7·5	11)8·6
F	8)34·45	7)70·4	9)5·42	12)36·11	11)10·4

Take answers to the fourth decimal place:

G	6)20·45	7)40	11)50	12)70·85	9)0·6

Take answers to the second SIGNIFICANT figure. Significant figures do not include the zeros which immediately follow the decimal point, unless there is a whole number before the decimal point, i.e. 0·00370 and 0·0408 are taken to the third significant figure.

H	5)0·055	4)0·17	7)0·086	9)10·01	6)6·58
I	8)3·21	9)20·75	12)3·61	12)9·71	11)12

Express each of these amounts to the nearest centimetre:

A	2·63 cm	0·0063 km	87·5 mm	3·784 m
B	2·25 m ÷ 10	0·837 m ÷ 10	0·0126 km ÷ 100	80·83 cm ÷ 100
C	0·006 km ÷ 7	32·66 m ÷ 8	180·7 mm ÷ 11	0·809 m ÷ 12

Express each of these amounts to the nearest litre:

D	0·608 *l*	7·05 *l*	0·0897 k*l*	0·3095 k*l*
E	0·7096 k*l* ÷ 10	290·7 *l* ÷ 100	17·66 *l* ÷ 9	126·9 *l* ÷ 12

F One seventh of the difference between 168·97 l and 0·305 kl

Express to the nearest gramme:

G	0·30703 kg	2·0939 g	760·8 mg	1·0607 kg
H	376·8 g ÷ 10	0·677 kg ÷ 7	986·54 mg ÷ 9	0·85 kg ÷ 12

I The average of 150·86 g + 203·65 g + 93·09 g + 108·93 g 139 g

Remember that with decimal money we are concerned with expressing amounts that can be represented by coins, the smallest being the halfpenny, which as a decimal would be written as '0·5p'.

Write which of these is nearest to 1p and which to $1\frac{1}{2}$p:

J	1·1p	1·4p	1·26p	1·24p	1·25p	1·37p

Write which of these is nearest to $1\frac{1}{2}$p and which to 2p:

K	1·7p	1·8p	1·75p	1·76p	1·73p	1·6p

Express these to the nearest halfpenny:

L	0·74p	3·6p	5·22p	8·25p	4·75p	3·96p
M	5·08p	10·3p	7·69p	4·73p	6·81p	7·69p

N	£0·067	£0·0831	£0·1377	£0·2581
O	£0·3026	£0·1067	£1·0309	£1·0078
P	£3·27 ÷ 5	£2·03 ÷ 6	£7·33 ÷ 4	£11·21 ÷ 6
Q	£20 ÷ 9	£30 ÷ 7	£10·50 ÷ 11	£15·25 ÷ 12
R	76p ÷ 9	$45\frac{1}{2}$p ÷ 8	£3·$84\frac{1}{2}$ ÷ 7	£3·28 ÷ 11

Divide. Take each answer to the fourth decimal place:

A	2 ÷ 3 =	1 ÷ 3 =	1 ÷ 6 =	2 ÷ 6 =	5 ÷ 6 =
B	1 ÷ 9 =	2 ÷ 9 =	3 ÷ 9 =	7 ÷ 9 =	8 ÷ 9 =
C	4 ÷ 11 =	2 ÷ 11 =	1 ÷ 11 =	6 ÷ 11 =	7 ÷ 11 =
D	5 ÷ 9 =	6 ÷ 9 =	8 ÷ 11 =	9 ÷ 11 =	10 ÷ 11 =

Special note: When an answer cannot be completed because a figure or group of figures repeat continuously, we place a dot over the repeating figure or figures.

The answers in Row **D** may be written like this:

$0{\cdot}\dot{5}$ $0{\cdot}\dot{6}$ $0{\cdot}\dot{7}\dot{2}$ $0{\cdot}\dot{8}\dot{1}$ $0{\cdot}\dot{9}\dot{0}$ These are known as recurring decimals.

Divide. Take each answer to the fourth decimal place:

E	$3\overline{)22{\cdot}1}$	$3\overline{)20{\cdot}2}$	$3\overline{)2{\cdot}5}$	$6\overline{)25{\cdot}3}$	$9\overline{)19{\cdot}9}$
F	$3\overline{)1{\cdot}415}$	$6\overline{)0{\cdot}55}$	$6\overline{)0{\cdot}013}$	$9\overline{)1{\cdot}87}$	$9\overline{)0{\cdot}365}$
G	$12\overline{)1{\cdot}1}$	$11\overline{)23}$	$11\overline{)33{\cdot}5}$	$11\overline{)128}$	$11\overline{)1{\cdot}9}$
H	$3\overline{)4{\cdot}\dot{4}}$	$3\overline{)6{\cdot}\dot{7}}$	$6\overline{)8{\cdot}\dot{8}}$	$3\overline{)6{\cdot}\dot{4}}$	$8\overline{)0{\cdot}11\dot{5}}$
I	$6\overline{)0{\cdot}2\dot{2}\dot{4}}$	$9\overline{)0{\cdot}12\dot{6}\dot{3}}$	$7\overline{)0{\cdot}16\dot{8}\dot{2}}$	$6\overline{)0{\cdot}3\dot{4}\dot{5}}$	$9\overline{)0{\cdot}6\dot{8}\dot{9}}$
J	$2\overline{)4{\cdot}\dot{3}}$	$2\overline{)6{\cdot}\dot{6}}$	$4\overline{)4{\cdot}\dot{6}\dot{4}}$	$5\overline{)2{\cdot}\dot{3}\dot{4}}$	$8\overline{)0{\cdot}2\dot{0}\dot{6}}$

Write these quantities CORRECT to the third decimal place:

A	0·3267	0·0566	1·1559	2·0168
B	0·4033	0·7012	2·0774	3·8925
C	0·0735	0·3906	2·4902	6·7906
D	0·0105	0·0705	0·0405	0·0908
E	0·2193	1·4396	3·0595	0·0296
F	0·5096	4·0099	0·3095	2·0998

Divide. Write answers correct to two places of decimals:

G $4\overline{)6{\cdot}315}$ $6\overline{)1{\cdot}298}$ $7\overline{)9{\cdot}02}$ $9\overline{)0{\cdot}77}$ $12\overline{)2{\cdot}96}$

H $5\overline{)0{\cdot}82}$ $7\overline{)0{\cdot}808}$ $8\overline{)0{\cdot}52}$ $8\overline{)0{\cdot}75}$ $11\overline{)1{\cdot}25}$

I $7\overline{)31{\cdot}561}$ $9\overline{)6{\cdot}343}$ $12\overline{)86{\cdot}42}$ $11\overline{)5{\cdot}6}$ $12\overline{)30{\cdot}1}$

J $8\overline{)60{\cdot}74}$ $11\overline{)45{\cdot}06}$ $12\overline{)1{\cdot}099}$ $9\overline{)0{\cdot}88}$ $12\overline{)13{\cdot}14}$

Divide. Write answers correct to three places of decimals:

K $6\overline{)0{\cdot}7\dot{5}}$ $8\overline{)3{\cdot}03}$ $7\overline{)9{\cdot}8}$ $7\overline{)7{\cdot}75}$ $9\overline{)8{\cdot}\dot{5}}$

L $7\overline{)0{\cdot}7\dot{6}}$ $12\overline{)84{\cdot}\dot{7}\dot{8}}$ $9\overline{)0{\cdot}2\dot{7}}$ $11\overline{)0{\cdot}107}$ $12\overline{)1{\cdot}1\dot{8}}$

Arrange the numbers in each group in order of magnitude:

A 340, 0·24, 2·4, 1·4, 40, 0·14

B 0·06, 3·0, 3·02, 0·5, 30·2, 30

Multiply each number in these pairs by 10:

C	1·2 and 4·3	1·2 and 0·43	0·7 and 7
D	3·5 and 0·275	0·8 and 0·08	0·6 and 60

Multiply each number in these pairs by 100:

E	2·34 and 43	0·75 and 53·2	0·08 and 1·9
F	1·07 and 0·6	0·04 and 3	6·25 and 7·5

Divide. Write answers only:

G	4 by 2	40 by 20	400 by 200	0·4 by 0·2
H	0·4 ÷ 0·4 =	0·8 ÷ 0·4 =	0·8 ÷ 0·2 =	8 ÷ 0·2 =
I	0·3 ÷ 0·3 =	0·6 ÷ 0·3 =	6 ÷ 0·3 =	6 ÷ 0·2 =
J	0·9 ÷ 0·3 =	0·09 ÷ 0·3 =	0·06 ÷ 0·2 =	0·08 ÷ 0·2 =
K	0·12 ÷ 0·3 =	0·12 ÷ 0·4 =	1·2 ÷ 0·3 =	1·2 ÷ 0·6 =
L	1·5 ÷ 5 =	0·15 ÷ 5 =	24 ÷ 0·6 =	0·24 ÷ 0·8 =

Divide:

M	0·4)4·8	0·6)24·6	0·7)1·47	0·5)3·05	4)8·04
N	0·4)246	0·5)153	1·1)25·3	1·2)42	1·2)30
O	0·6)0·084	0·7)0·098	0·9)0·009	0·8)0·04	1·2)0·09

Divide. Take answers to the second decimal place:

A $2{\cdot}1\overline{)44{\cdot}1}$ $2{\cdot}3\overline{)27{\cdot}6}$ $3{\cdot}1\overline{)68{\cdot}6}$ $1{\cdot}8\overline{)57{\cdot}8}$

B $0{\cdot}21\overline{)6{\cdot}72}$ $21\overline{)48{\cdot}3}$ $0{\cdot}22\overline{)9{\cdot}46}$ $0{\cdot}32\overline{)1{\cdot}073}$

Take answers to the third decimal place:

C $0{\cdot}25\overline{)0{\cdot}1\dot{3}}$ $3{\cdot}4\overline{)0{\cdot}0\dot{7}}$ $0{\cdot}12\overline{)0{\cdot}\dot{0}\dot{6}}$ $2{\cdot}6\overline{)1{\cdot}08}$

Take answer correct to the second significant figure:

D $37\overline{)8{\cdot}55}$ $0{\cdot}52\overline{)0{\cdot}703}$ $4{\cdot}8\overline{)0{\cdot}16\dot{8}}$ $3{\cdot}1\overline{)6{\cdot}326}$

Take answers correct to first decimal place:

E $0{\cdot}32\overline{)0{\cdot}73}$ $0{\cdot}24\overline{)5{\cdot}\dot{0}\dot{6}}$ $0{\cdot}36\overline{)0{\cdot}745}$ $0{\cdot}85\overline{)221}$

Accuracy with recurring decimals

Add:

A	$2{\cdot}357$	$6{\cdot}75$	$3{\cdot}869$	$0{\cdot}0708$	$0{\cdot}036$
	$0{\cdot}7\dot{6}$	$13{\cdot}875$	$0{\cdot}\dot{0}\dot{9}$	$0{\cdot}26\dot{9}$	$0{\cdot}3\dot{7}$
	$0{\cdot}08$	$0{\cdot}6\dot{8}$	$0{\cdot}76\dot{3}$	$0{\cdot}0\dot{3}\dot{6}$	$0{\cdot}008$
	$3{\cdot}297$	$5{\cdot}69$	$0{\cdot}279$	$0{\cdot}623$	$0{\cdot}079$

Subtract:

B	$2{\cdot}362$	$6{\cdot}3$	$0{\cdot}256$	$3{\cdot}752$	$0{\cdot}2708$
	$-1{\cdot}0\dot{8}$	$-2{\cdot}\dot{6}$	$-0{\cdot}\dot{0}\dot{9}$	$-1{\cdot}0\dot{4}\dot{2}$	$-0{\cdot}1\dot{5}$

C	$0{\cdot}305$	8	$0{\cdot}7$	$1{\cdot}568$	$0{\cdot}6\dot{4}\dot{8}$
	$-0{\cdot}\dot{1}\dot{8}$	$-5{\cdot}7\dot{6}\dot{2}$	$-0{\cdot}05\dot{9}$	$-0{\cdot}\dot{9}\dot{0}$	$-0{\cdot}1\dot{5}$

Multiply:

D	$2{\cdot}\dot{4}$	$1{\cdot}\dot{8}\dot{1}$	$0{\cdot}6\dot{3}\dot{9}$	$0{\cdot}3\dot{2}$	$0{\cdot}0\dot{5}$
	$\times\ 5$	$\times\ 6$	$\times\ 7$	$\times\ 0{\cdot}9$	$\times\ 0{\cdot}8$

E	$16{\cdot}3$	$2{\cdot}05\dot{8}$	$3{\cdot}125$	$3{\cdot}\dot{2}\dot{7}$	$0{\cdot}8\dot{5}$
	$\times\ 0{\cdot}\dot{6}$	$\times\ 0{\cdot}17$	$\times\ 2{\cdot}\dot{3}$	$\times\ 1{\cdot}8$	$\times\ 0{\cdot}8\dot{5}$

Decimals and fractions

5·3 $=5$ whole units and 3 tenths or $5\frac{3}{10}$

0·37 $=3$ tenths and 7 hundredths or $\frac{3}{10}+\frac{7}{100}=\frac{30}{100}+\frac{7}{100}=\frac{37}{100}$

0·01 $=1$ hundredth or $\frac{1}{100}$

$0{\cdot}213=\frac{2}{10}+\frac{1}{100}+\frac{3}{1000}=\frac{200}{1000}+\frac{10}{1000}+\frac{3}{1000}=\frac{213}{1000}$

From this it will be seen that a decimal can be changed to an equal fraction having a denominator of 1 followed by as many zeros as there are places in the decimal.

Complete these:

A $0{\cdot}7=\frac{7}{\quad}$ $\quad 0{\cdot}57=\frac{57}{\quad}$ $\quad 0{\cdot}07=\frac{7}{\quad}$ $\quad 0{\cdot}007=\frac{7}{\quad}$ $\quad 2{\cdot}37=2$

Change these decimals into vulgar fractions:

B 0·43 1·17 0·09 3·01 0·207 0·003

C 2·9 20·7 0·0601 4·03 10·89 20·077

Change these decimals into vulgar fractions in their lowest terms:

D 0·6 2·6 1·32 1·68 2·55 1·05

E 0·04 0·044 3·75 2·604 1·125 10·065

Recurring decimals—When changing recurring decimals into fractions one must allow for the incomplete part of the decimal. Look carefully at these:

$0{\cdot}\dot{6}$ can be written as 0·6666 . . .

$10\times0{\cdot}\dot{6}=6{\cdot}6666\ldots$

Take away $1\times0{\cdot}\dot{6}=0{\cdot}6666\ldots$

Therefore $9\times0{\cdot}\dot{6}=6$

and $0{\cdot}\dot{6}=\frac{6}{9}=\frac{2}{3}$

$0{\cdot}2\dot{7}$ can be written as 0·27777 . . .

$100\times0{\cdot}2\dot{7}=27{\cdot}7777\ldots$

Take away $10\times0{\cdot}2\dot{7}=2{\cdot}7777\ldots$

Therefore $90\times0{\cdot}2\dot{7}=25$

and $0{\cdot}2\dot{7}=\frac{25}{90}$

Note – To change a recurring decimal into a fraction:

1 Subtract the number formed by the non-recurring digits from the number formed by all of the digits in the decimal: that gives you the NUMERATOR.
2 To obtain the DENOMINATOR write a 9 for each recurring digit followed by 0 for each non-recurring digit.

Change these decimals into vulgar fractions in their lowest terms:

A $0{\cdot}\dot{3}$ $0{\cdot}\dot{4}$ $0{\cdot}3\dot{6}$ $1{\cdot}4\dot{8}$ $1{\cdot}1\dot{6}$ $2{\cdot}2\dot{9}$

B $1{\cdot}6\dot{3}$ $2{\cdot}8\dot{2}$ $5{\cdot}0\dot{3}$ $0{\cdot}14\dot{8}$ $0{\cdot}27\dot{2}$ $3{\cdot}08\dot{3}$

C $0{\cdot}2\dot{2}\dot{4}$ $0{\cdot}6\dot{1}\dot{2}$ $2{\cdot}7\dot{0}\dot{3}$ $0{\cdot}\dot{2}\dot{7}$ $2{\cdot}\dot{5}\dot{7}$ $4{\cdot}\dot{6}\dot{3}$

Complete:

D $\frac{2}{5}=\frac{4}{\ }=$ $2\div5=$ $\frac{3}{5}=\frac{\ }{10}=$ $3\div5=$

Note—To change a vulgar fraction into a decimal fraction divide the denominator into the numerator.

Change these fractions into decimals: do not take answers beyond the fourth decimal place:

E $\frac{1}{5}$ $\frac{1}{2}$ $\frac{4}{5}$ $\frac{1}{4}$ $\frac{3}{8}$ $\frac{5}{8}$

F $\frac{3}{20}$ $\frac{1}{6}$ $\frac{4}{9}$ $\frac{5}{12}$ $\frac{3}{11}$ $\frac{5}{7}$

G $1\frac{3}{4}$ $2\frac{7}{20}$ $1\frac{7}{8}$ $3\frac{9}{20}$ $\frac{2}{3}$ $\frac{11}{20}$

H $2\frac{1}{3}$ $1\frac{5}{6}$ $5\frac{5}{11}$ $2\frac{3}{7}$ $3\frac{7}{9}$ $6\frac{7}{12}$

I $\frac{2}{15}$ $3\frac{5}{16}$ $5\frac{3}{14}$ $7\frac{9}{11}$ $4\frac{3}{21}$ $2\frac{7}{30}$

J $\frac{7}{8}$ $2\frac{7}{16}$ $1\frac{17}{20}$ $3\frac{1}{15}$ $5\frac{19}{100}$ $4\frac{6}{13}$